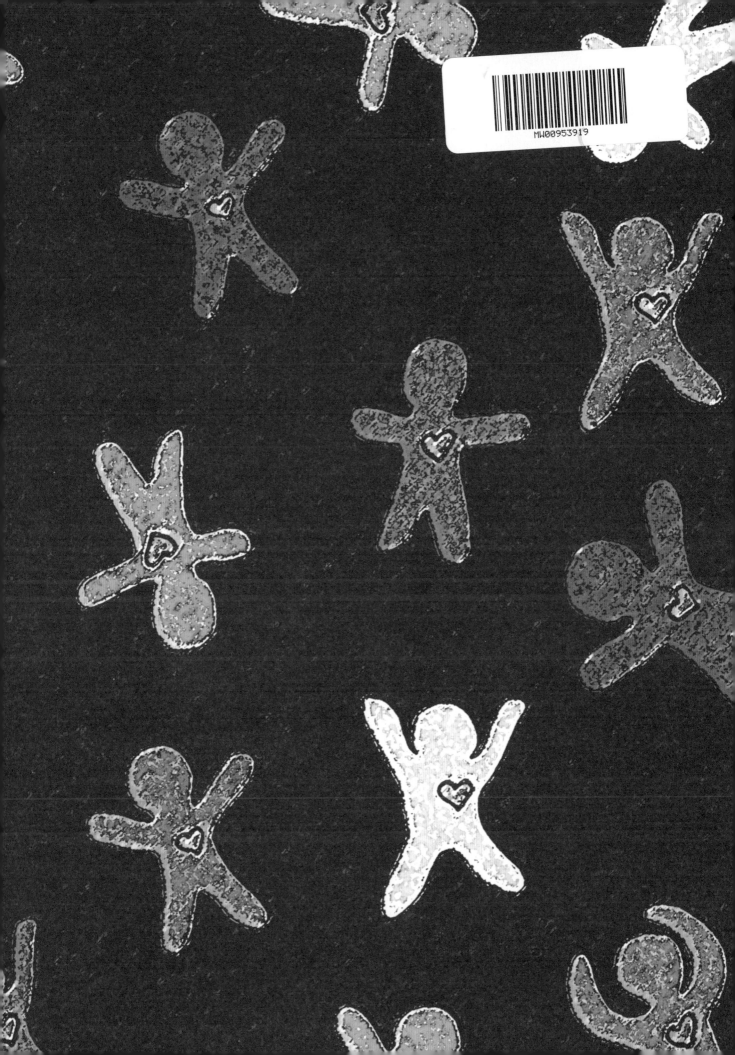

MW00953919

I am who I think I am...

Written and Illustrated by
Adrianne Atkins, Eric Atkins and Tina Brunson

For information write:

Inner Peace Publishing
P.O. Box 1538
Cedar Park, TX 78630-1538

Or call: (512) 415-5764
Website: www.innerpeacepublishing.com
E-mail: info@innerpeacepublishing.com

If you are unable to order this book from your local
bookseller, you may order directly from the publisher.
Quantity discounts are available.

First U.S. Edition, 2002.

Library of Congress Catalog Card Number: 2002105926

ISBN 0-9720647-1-0

Printed in Hong Kong.

DEAR BAELEN,

This book is dedicated to you.

ALL THE BEST

YORK

Dear Pare

It is our heartfelt wish that this book

open a channel of deep communica

these pages, we have attempted to

expose the wonder and beauty of

growth into a life of inner pea

provoking thought, insight a

will encourage a loving attitu

vivid imagination, responsibil

We want children to know t

will give the greatest tool of

We suggest using each page to ev

Explore ideas, concrete examples,

bring to mind. Get creative,

have fun explor

Please know this book is a

hear these phrases directed

they apply equa

You, too, ca

cher/Friend,

d as a door of opportunity to help
ween you and your child. Within
vn a simple path that will not only
also serve as a foundation for
piness and joy. It is our belief that
areness from the earliest years
fidence, curiosity, exploration, a
esty and the joy of giving freely .
ting in touch with themselves
living life — *a nurtured soul.*

og between you and your child.
sibilities that each phrase may
ur imaginations and, most of all,
h topic.

ended for you. If you did not
u as a child, hear them now —
everyone.

anything!!!

We are all one

Wisdom comes from within.

All I need i

What do I believe?

Wisdom come

We are all connected.

already inside of me...

elieve in
myself.

We all have t

ne feelings. I listen to other's needs. How can I help today? Now.

I help others.

I open my mind.

I open my heart.

I open my eyes.

I create who I am.

What will I change?

Free is love.

I love a
uncondi

What does love feel like?

Love frees your Spirit!

things
nally.

Love is free

The whole universe
is my playground.

Where would I like to play? How big is the universe? We are all a part of the universe.

Life is full
of ups and
downs.

I enjoy
the ride.

Giving is the greatest art. Share the wealth.

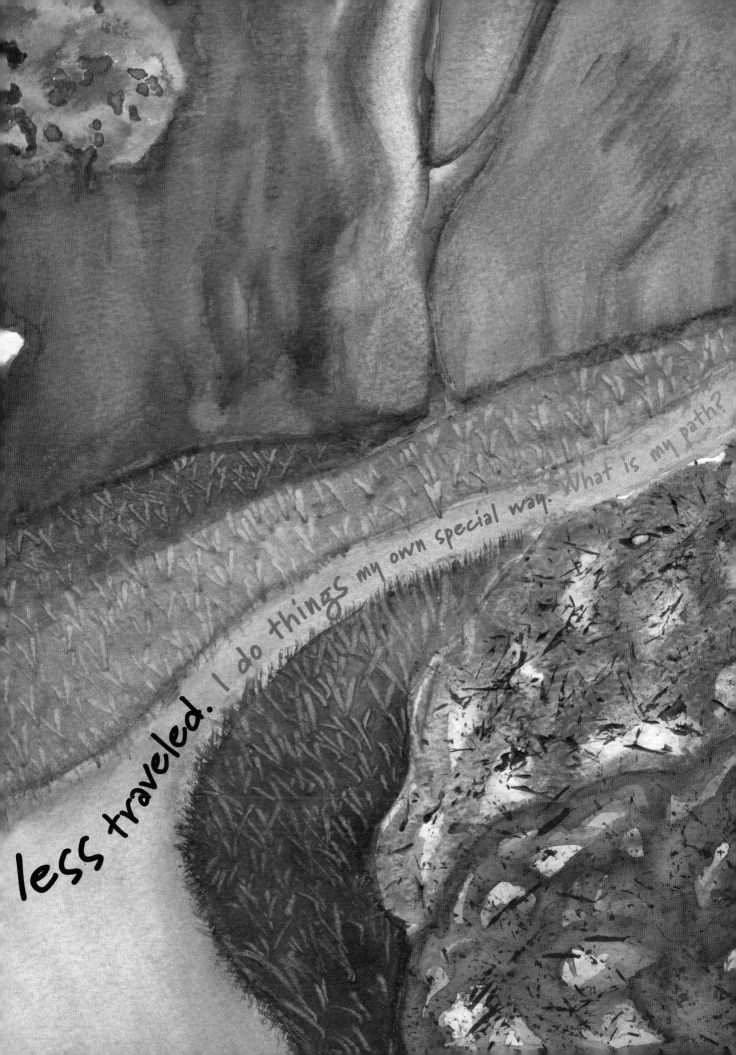

less traveled. I do things my own special way. What is my path?

I can do ANYTHING!

I am who I thin[k]

I am always changing.

I am...so I think great thoughts.

My thoughts...

Inner Peace Publishing
P.O. Box 1538
Cedar Park, TX 78630-1538

www.innerpeacepublishing.com

Check out our website for other items featuring
artwork from this book.

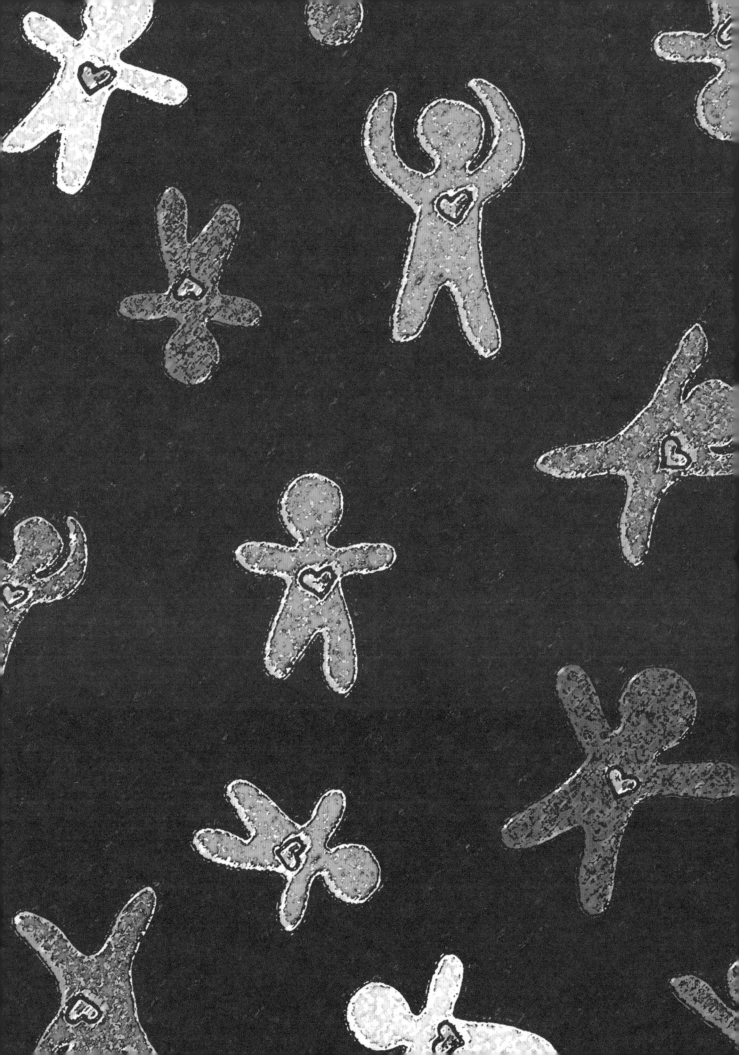